Dedicated to Mr. Julian,
an awesome teacher
—N. S.

website www.zoebeautee.com

NIVEA'S
BLUE
GUITAR

Written by **Nivea**
and **Carline Smothers**

Illustrated by **Fuuji Takashi**

My parents got me a guitar
for Christmas!

Not just any guitar.
A big shiny BLUE guitar.

Oh, how I picture myself playing this guitar. It will be like the deep **BLUE** sea that flows effortlessly.

Or, the clear BLUE sky...

...that takes me away when the breeze goes by.

Maybe, it will be like a great **BLUE** whale,
echoing in the ocean.

Or, a BLUE jay
singing beautiful melodies,
soaring high in the sky.

As I began to strum on my guitar, it did not sound as I imagined.

"All you need is a little practice
and you will be just fine," my parents said.
"You start guitar lessons on Saturday!"

Today is my first day
in guitar class.

Mr. Julian teaches us the parts of a guitar. There are six strings.

E-A-D-G-B-E

We learn how to tune our guitars.
When I loosen the strings,
it makes the pitch go down.
When I tighten the strings,
it makes the pitch go up.

He teaches us how to
read notes to play music.

My thumb and fingers start
to blister up and hurt. Mr. Julian gives
me a round red pick
to help when I play.

He tells me to do
spider fingers, rapidly
moving my fingers

to strengthen my
hand while practicing.

After a few classes the
blister on my thumb and
fingers goes away.

I'M GETTING BETTER AND
BETTER EVERY DAY.

Now playing my guitar
is like a great   whale,
swimming in the deep BLUE sea,

and a BLUE jay
flying high in the clear blue sky,
singing effortlessly.

No need to imagine
because I can go far.
All I need is a little confidence
and my big shiny BLUE guitar.

What's your favorite instrument?

LEARN KREYÓL

Ble ~ Blue

Gita ~ Guitar

CPSIA information can be obtained
at www.ICGtesting.com
Printed in the USA
LVHW070711151222
735276LV00008B/224